This book is dedicated with love to my two children:
Kaliah and Karter Henry.

May you always find contentment and joy in pursuing
and achieving your heart desires.

ISBN 978-0-578-84093-2

Text by Kashama Leo-Henry
Illustrations by Gerry O'Neill

First printing edition 2021.

Daddies and Uncles and More, Oh My!

Written by Kashama Leo-Henry

Illustrated by Gerry O'Neill

This is Daddy. He has a big heart.
Daddy showed me love right from the start.
Daddy gave me kisses on my toes.
Now that I'm growing, he kisses my nose.

Granddaddy always saves the day,
whether he is near or far away.
A role model that I look up to.
He taught me how to be kind and true.
The values he taught me remain in my heart,
whether we are near or far apart.

This is my uncle, so loving and strong.
Uncle teaches me what is right and wrong.
I love when we go to the park to play.
Oh, what a joy! Hooray! Hooray!
I'm always excited for the fun we share.
We sing and dance, and we jump in the air.

This is my cousin. He is called Dave.
He helps me to be strong and brave.
When it is time to visit the doctor,
he gives me a call. Yes, that's for sure.
The kind nurse says, "It's time for your shot."
I hear him whisper, "It won't sting a lot."
"Close your eyes, and count to ten.
It's over! I bet you can do it again!"

A special shout out to my brother, Ace.
He loses board games but wins when we race.
He is a protector and my dear friend.
I know that on him, I can depend.
Whenever I am feeling sad and down,
my brother knows how to fix my frown.
He gives me a hug—oh-so tight!
He tells me everything will be all right.

This is a family friend we call Tom.
He gives support to my dad and my mom.
When Daddy can't take me for a swim,
Tom shows up, glowing with a beam.
He is caring, supportive, and strong.
He makes me feel that I always belong.

There are other men in my family too.
Adopted fathers and step-daddies too.
They give plenty of hugs, kisses, and treats.
Because of them, my birthdays are neat.
Playdates, sports, school engagements, and more.
These men always show up in galore!

Daddies and uncles and more, oh my!
I'm lucky to have them to help me fly.

Thanks for the bedtime stories at night,
for being an alarm at morning light.
Providing three meals to eat in a day
and two healthy snacks along the way.
Forever grateful for all that you do . . .
Your influence, character, and presence too!

There are many men—fathers, brothers, uncles, cousins, friends, and more—who nurture and support the well-being of children. This book is designed to highlight the contributions of Black fathers and male role models in healthy child development. Despite the systemic barriers they face, these men play an important role in raising happy, healthy children. Follow along as our young narrator, Lili, shows appreciation to the wonderful male role models who help her learn and grow.

CPSIA information can be obtained
at www.ICGtesting.com
Printed in the USA
BVHW020951150421
605028BV00004B/108

9 780578 840932